Eat for Goals!
Football Heroes' Healthy Recipes

0 9 JUN 2014
2 9 JUL 2016

Eat for Goals !

This paperback edition is published in the UK in 2010 by
A&C Black Publishers Ltd
36 Soho Square
London W1D 3QY
www.acblack.com

A&C BLACK

Copyright © UEFA 2010

ISBN 978 14081 3067 4

A CIP catalogue record for this record is available from the British Library.

Note: Whilst every effort has been made to ensure that the content of this book is technically accurate and as sound as possible, neither the author nor the publishers can accept responsibility for any injury or loss sustained as a result of use of this material.

Manufactured by C&C Offset Printing Co, China.

This book is produced using paper that is made from wood grown in managed, sustainable forests. It is natural, renewable and recyclable. The logging and manufacturing processes conform to the environmental regulations of the country of origin.

Eat for Goals!

Football Heroes' Healthy Recipes

UEFA
we care

 WORLD HEART FEDERATION®

 EUROPEAN COMMISSION

Contents

4

 6 Diet and Exercise

 10 The Players

 12 Abbas Suwan

 14 Tabbouleh

 16 Birgit Prinz

 18 Breakfast

 20 Carles Puyol

 22 Pasta with Pesto and Grilled Vegetables

 24 Cathrine Paaske Sørensen

 26 Chicken Salad with Garlic Curried Yoghurt Dressing

 28 Fabio Cannavaro

 30 Pasta alla Siciliana

 32 Frank Lampard

 34 Spinach with Fruit and Nuts

 36 Heurelho da Silva Gomes

 38 Pasta and Tropical Mixed Salad

 40 Kelly Smith

 42 Chicken Salad Sandwich with Lime Yoghurt

 44 Kenny Miller

 46 Fresh Fruit Salad

 48 Marcos Antonio Senna da Silva

50 Swordfish and Vegetables

52 Ruud van Nistelrooy

 54 Salmon Grilled with Cloves, served with Vegetables

 56 Steven Gerrard

 58 Crunchy Sea Bream with Herbs

 60 Yoann Gourcuff

 62 Spaghetti al'Arrabiata with Vegetables and Tuna

 66 Water

 68 Vegetables

 70 Fruit

 72 Pasta, Rice, Potatoes

 74 Cereals, Bread

 76 Eggs, Pulses, Nuts, Seeds

 78 Fish, Chicken, Meat

 80 Milk, Yoghurt, Cheese

 82 Food and Drinks High in Fat, Sugar and/or Salt

 84 Michel Platini

 86 Pekka Puska

 88 Androulla Vassiliou

 90 Glossary

 92 Index

 94 Working for Goals

 95 A book with more than one goal!

5

Diet and Exercise

Eat well and be active every day.

Balance energy IN
(what we eat and drink)

with energy OUT
(how much we exercise).

Aim for **variety** and a
good **balance** of food and drink.

Enjoy a sport –
but it doesn't always
have to be competitive!

Lots of vegetables, fruits – aim for 5 a day!

Satisfy thirst
with water!

Be active at home,
in your community, at school
for 1 hour a day.

... Diet and Exercise

Try to include one portion of bread, rice, pasta, potatoes or cereal with your meals – **they are good for energy.**

Do some **activities** with family and friends!

Add some lean meat, fish, chicken, eggs, pulses, lentils, nuts or seeds and milk, yoghurt, cheese.

Choose activities you really enjoy doing.

Enjoy all of these foods by preparing and eating them with little or no added **fat, sugar or salt.**

Limit those foods and drinks that are **high in calories,** fat, sugar or salt (sodium).

Drink **water regularly.** It's a calorie-free, sugar-free and caffeine-free way to quench your thirst.

The Players

Name Suwan
First name Abbas
National team Israel
Date of birth 27/1/76
Place of birth Sakhnin (Israel)
Previous clubs Ihoud Bnei Sakhnin FC, Maccabi Haifa FC,
Hapoël Ironi Kiryat Shmona FC (Israel)
Current club Ihoud Bnei Sakhnin FC (Israel)
Player position Midfielder

Name Paaske Sørensen
First name Cathrine
National team Denmark
Date of birth 14/6/78
Place of birth Dannemare, Island of Lolland (Denmark)
Previous clubs Rudbjerg BK, Brøndby IF, Linköpings FC
(Denmark), Sydney FC (Australia)
Current club Fortuna Hjørring FC (Denmark)
Player position Midfielder

Name Prinz
First name Birgit
National team Germany
Date of birth 25/10/77
Place of birth Frankfurt am Main (Germany)
Previous clubs FSV Frankfurt, 1. FFC Frankfurt Germany),
Carolina Courage (USA)
Current club 1. FFC Frankfurt (Germany)
Player position Attacker

Name Cannavaro
First name Fabio
National team Italy
Date of birth 13/9/73
Place of birth Naples (Italy)
Previous clubs SSC Napoli, Parma FC, FC Internazionale Milano,
Juventus (Italy), Real Madrid CF (Spain)
Current Club Juventus (Italy)
Player position Defender

Name Puyol
First name Carles
National team Spain
Date of birth 13/4/78
Place of birth Lleida (Spain)
Previous clubs –
Current club FC Barcelona (Spain)
Player position Defender

Name Lampard
First name Frank
National team England
Date of birth 20/6/78
Place of birth Romford (England)
Previous clubs West Ham United FC (England)
Current club Chelsea FC (England)
Player position Midfielder

Name Senna da Silva
First name Marcos Antonio
National team Spain
Date of birth 17/7/76
Place of birth São Paulo (Brazil)
Previous clubs São Caetano (Brazil)
Current club FC Villarreal (Spain)
Player position Midfielder

Name Da Silva Gomes
First name Heurelho
National team Brazil
Date of birth 15/2/81
Place of birth João Pinheiro (Brazil)
Previous clubs Cruzeiro EC (Brazil)
Current club Tottenham Hotspur FC (England)
Player position Goalkeeper

Name van Nistelrooy
First name Ruud
National team Netherlands
Date of birth 1/7/76
Place of birth Oss (Netherlands)
Previous clubs FC Den Bosch, SC Heerenveen,
  PSV Eindhoven (Netherlands),
  Manchester United FC (England),
  Real Madrid CF (Spain)
Current club Hamburg SV (Germany)
Player position Attacker

Name Smith
First name Kelly
National team England
Date of birth 29/10/78
Place of birth Watford (England)
Previous clubs Arsenal LFC (England),
  Seton Hall University,
  Philadelphia Charge,
  New Jersey Wildcats (USA),
  Arsenal LFC (England)
Current club Boston Breakers (USA)
Player position Attacker

Name Gerrard
First name Steven
National team England
Date of birth 30/5/80
Place of birth Whiston, Liverpool (England)
Previous clubs –
Current club FC Liverpool (England)
Player position Midfielder

Name Miller
First name Kenny
National team Scotland
Date of birth 23/12/79
Place of birth Edinburgh (Scotland)
Previous clubs Hibernian, Glasgow Rangers, Wolverhampton,
  Celtic Glasgow, Derby County (Scotland)
Current club Glasgow Rangers (Scotland)
Player position Goalkeeper

Name Gourcuff
First name Yoann
National team France
Date of birth 11/7/86
Place of birth Ploemeur (France)
Previous clubs FC Lorient, Stade Rennais FC (France),
  AC Milan (Italy)
Current club FC Girondins de Bordeaux (France)
Player position Midfielder

Abbas Suwan

For lunch I like:

lentil soup

pasta

fresh tomato sauce

grilled chicken breast or fish

How does a healthy diet help me play well?

I feel energetic, strong and less injury-prone. Pasta 2.5 hours before exercise is a great source of energy.

WORLD HEART FEDERATION®

Food I love to eat?

Honey and nigella (black cumin – has amazing therapeutic and healing power).

Favourite dish when I was a kid?

My mother's famous rice with pine nuts, walnuts and beef.

Who cooks my favourite food?

My wife!

How's my cooking?

I can cook great pasta.

UEFA
we care

Tabbouleh
Abbas Suwan

Couscous
(quick-cook) 150 g

Cucumber
½, chopped

Tomatoes
2, chopped

Virgin olive oil,
family-made!!!
½ tbsp

Parsley
½ tbsp, chopped

Mint
½ tbsp, chopped

Lettuce
4 large leaves

Lemon ½

Put the couscous in a dish.
Add twice as much boiling
water as couscous.

Cover, leave to
stand and cool.

Mix the couscous,
cucumber, mint, parsley
and tomatoes.

Place each portion
in a lettuce leaf.

Use the olive oil and
squeezed lemon for
the dressing.

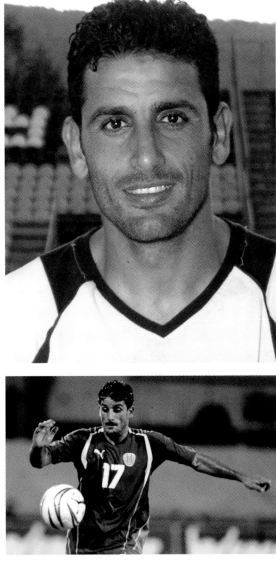

Cooking time
5 mins

Preparation time
15 mins

Serves
4
children

Per child portion

Energy	669 kj
	158 kcal
Protein	5 g
Carbohydrate	31 g
Fat	2 g

Birgit Prinz

Ingredients I love to eat?

fish

vegetables

chicken

chocolate

fruit

WORLD HEART FEDERATION®

FOR a FRESH drink I like:

milk, fruit

Who cooks MY Favourite Food?

Mum and Dad

How is MY cooking?

Very good!

Breakfast
Birgit Prinz

Milk
125 ml

Banana
½, sliced

Strawberries
4–5, sliced

Cereal
One bowl or about 30 g

Put the cereal
in a bowl or
glass,
add the sliced
strawberries,
bananas,
and milk
and enjoy!

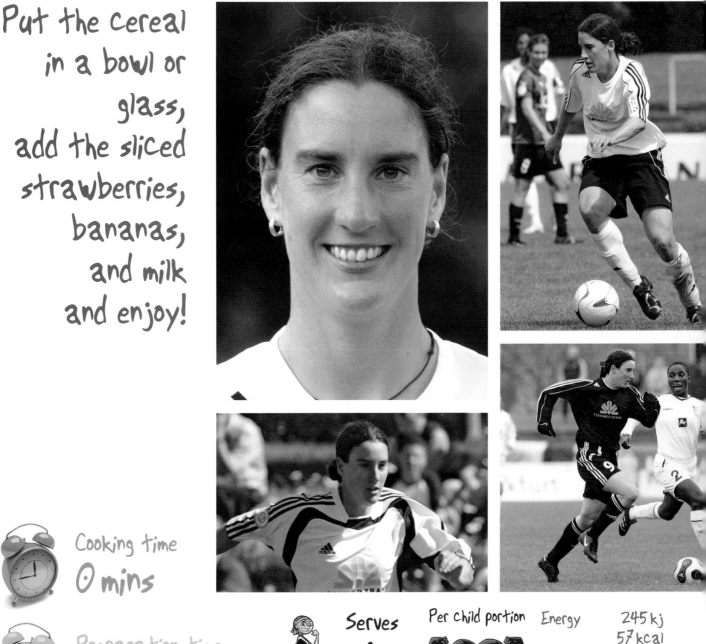

 Cooking time
0 mins

Preparation time
5 mins

 Serves
1
child

Per child portion

Energy	245 kj
	57 kcal
Protein	5 g
Carbohydrate	11 g
Fat	0.8 g

Carles Puyol

My Favourite Food After a Game?

sushi

3 ingredients I love?

pasta, fish, fruit

WORLD HEART FEDERATION®

FOR a FRESH drink I like?

+ +

strawberries, banana and mango
as a milkshake or in a smoothie

Who cooks
MY FAVOURITE FOOD?

My wife
and my mum

HOW'S MY cooking?

Natural and grilled!!!

FCB

UEFA
we care

Pasta with Pesto and Grilled Vegetables
Carles Puyol

Pasta
160 g (dried), cooked al dente

Red onion
1, sliced

Pesto
home-made or
healthy ready-made
2 tbsp

Tomatoes
2, sliced

Olive oil
1 tbsp

Aubergine
1, sliced

Red pepper
1, sliced (remove seeds)

Spread the chopped vegetables onto a grill pan or flat roasting tray, pour 1 tbsp of olive oil over them. Stir so they are coated with the oil, place under a grill or in an oven heated to 200°C, grill/roast, turning them a couple of times until soft.

Pour a boiled kettleful of water into a medium to large pan, making sure there is plenty of water for the amount of pasta. Bring it back to the boil over a highish heat. Tip the pasta into the water, add some olive oil to prevent them from sticking together. Give it a stir and continue to boil everything for about 5-10 minutes depending on the size and quality of the pasta. Drain the pasta in a colander.

Mix the pesto and grilled/ roasted vegetables with the cooked pasta.

Serve!

Cooking time
20 mins

Preparation time
30 mins

Serves
4
children

Per child portion

Energy	1130 kj
	268 kcal
Protein	9 g
Carbohydrate	38 g
Fat	10 g

Cathrine Paaske Sørensen

How does a healthy diet help me play well?

It gives me a lot of energy.

For lunch I like open sandwiches with lots of good toppings, such as:

roast beef

egg

fish

avocado

tomato

WORLD HEART FEDERATION®

FOR a FResh dRink
I like: fruitshake with

strawberries

oranges

banana

melon

Who cooks my Favourite Food?

My mum and my favourite Thai restaurant!

MY cooking?
Quick and good!

UEFA
we care

Chicken Salad
with Garlic Curried Yoghurt Dressing
Cathrine Paaske Sørensen

Tomato
1, chopped

Avocado
1, peeled and chopped

Cucumber
½, sliced

Sweetcorn
1, cooked, kernels stripped
from the cob

Sundried tomato
1, finely chopped

Curry powder
1 tbsp

Pepper
1 tsp

Chicken breasts
2, grilled and sliced

Red onion
½, sliced

Natural yoghurt
2 small pots

Garlic
1 clove, crushed

Make a salad dressing by mixing the yoghurt, garlic, pepper and curry powder.

Make a salad to your taste with the other ingredients.

Cooking time
10 mins

Preparation time
15 mins

Serves
4
children

Per child portion

Energy	1287 kj
	308 kcal
Protein	22 g
Carbohydrate	17 g
Fat	17 g

Fabio Cannavaro

After a game I like:

home-made pizza with
fresh tomatoes and mozzarella

Ingredients I really love?

(Parma ham,
pasta,
mozzarella)

How does a healthy diet help me play well?

It's the fuel for my performance. If you don't use the right fuel, you can't perform at the top level!

Favourite dish when I was a kid?

Rigatoni alla Siciliana.

Who cooks my favourite food?

My wife!

My cooking?

Good!! I'm good at pasta, fish and steak.

JUVENTUS

UEFA
we care

Pasta alla Siciliana
Fabio Cannavaro

Tomatoes
6, chopped

Aubergines
2 small, cubed

Garlic
4 cloves, crushed

Pasta
160 g (dried),
cooked al dente

Basil
handful, chopped

Olive oil
1 tbsp

Black olives
12, chopped

Capers
2 tbsp

Onions
2, chopped

To cook pasta well, use lots of boiling water in a large pot and try not to overcook it. Allow about 1 litre of water per 100 grams of dried pasta.

Bring the water to a full rolling boil in a large pan and add a few drops of oil. Add the pasta all at one go and stir it around just once to separate it. Don't put a lid on the pan but keep the pasta boiling gently.

Set the timer for 10 minutes or as suggested on the packet. But keep an eye on the pasta as it cooks and taste it after about 5 minutes. The pasta is cooked when it is al dente or has just a bit of bite to it. Stop cooking straight away and drain the pasta through a colander (leaving a little water clinging to the pasta to prevent sticking).

Fry the onions in a little olive oil until soft, add the garlic and aubergine, cook for 5 minutes, add the other vegetables, cook for further 5 minutes, mix the pasta and vegetables, add the basil, olives and capers.

Enjoy!!

Cooking time
10 mins

Preparation time
15 mins

Serves
4
children

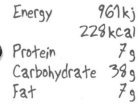

Per child portion

Energy	961 kj
	228 kcal
Protein	7 g
Carbohydrate	38 g
Fat	7 g

Frank Lampard

For breakfast before a game I like:

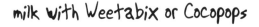

milk with Weetabix or Cocopops

Ingredients I really love?

I like to eat pasta with many sauces – and especially pasta with tomato, mozzarella and chillies.

How does a healthy diet help me to play well?

I have more energy every day, and especially before matches.

For a fresh drink I like:

fresh orange and lemon juice

Who cooks my favourite food?

My girlfriend Elen!

How is my cooking?

My cooking is not bad at all. I can cook a range of dishes from pasta to oven-cooked fish. I also love to make roast vegetables.

UEFA
we care

Spinach with FRUiT and NUts
Frank Lampard

Pine nuts
1 heaped tbsp / 20 g

Raisins
2 tbsp / 36 g

Olive oil
½ tbsp

Spinach
180 g

Dried apricots
6 / 64 g

Rinse and dry the spinach.

Heat a heavy or non-stick frying pan and add pine nuts to toast, gently stirring from time to time. Keep an eye on them and when they are just browned, remove them from the pan.

Add ½ tbsp of oil to the same pan, when the oil is hot but not smoking, stir in the raisins and apricots to heat through and soften a little.

Add the spinach to the pan with the dried fruit and stir just until the spinach is wilted a little. Stir in the toasted pine nuts and serve as a vegetable side dish.

Cooking time
5 mins

Preparation time
5 mins

Serves
4
children

Per child portion

Energy	473 kj
	112 kcal
Protein	3 g
Carbohydrate	14 g
Fat	5 g

Heurelho da Silva Gomes

For breakfast before a game I like:

yoghurt and fruit, with fresh orange juice

After a game I like:

WORLD HEART FEDERATION®

salad, beef and potatoes

How does a healthy diet help me play well?

I have a clear mind and my body feels great!

Favourite dish when I was a kid?

milk soup with bread

Who cooks my favourite food?

My wife and my mum!

My cooking?

I try to help in the kitchen...

TOTTENHAM HOTSPUR

37

UEFA
we care

Pasta and Tropical Mixed Salad

Heurelho da Silva Gomes

Pasta
160 g (dried), cooked al
dente, cooled

Mango
1, stone removed and
finely chopped

Kiwis
2, peeled,
sliced and cut into small pieces

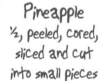

Pineapple
½, peeled, cored,
sliced and cut
into small pieces

Tomatoes
3, chopped

Dressing
your favourite to taste
about 1 tbsp

Red onion
1, finely chopped

Brazil nuts
3 or to taste

Bring a large pot of water to the boil, add a few drops of oil, then add the pasta. Bring the water back to the boil and cook with the lid off until the pasta is al dente or for 5–10 minutes, as per cooking instructions on the packet.

Mix all, add the dressing and enjoy it!!

Cooking time
10 mins

Preparation time
15 mins

Serves
4
children

Per child portion

Energy	1049 kj
	250 kcal
Protein	6g
Carbohydrate	47g
Fat	6g

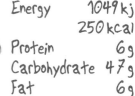

Kelly Smith

Ingredients I love to eat:

apples

bananas

pasta

chicken

tomatoes

carrots

onions

lettuce

WORLD HEART FEDERATION®

How does a healthy diet help me play well?

I get the right amount of **energy** into my body to help me perform at the **highest** level.

Who cooks my favourite food?

My mum!

How is your cooking?

I know the basics and I find it relaxing to make a meal and sit down with team-mates to eat and enjoy it.

we care

Chicken Salad Sandwich with Lime Yoghurt
Kelly Smith

Low-fat natural yoghurt
125 g

Olive bread
4 slices, lightly toasted

Lime
½

Chicken breasts
2, sliced horizontally

Lettuce
4 small leaves

Tomatoes
2, sliced

Grill the chicken slices to taste. Squeeze the lime juice into the yoghurt and stir. Spread the yoghurt on the olive bread, add the chicken slices, tomato and lettuce.

Cooking time
10 mins

Preparation time
10 mins

Serves
4
children

Per child portion

Energy	748 kj
	176 kcal
Protein	21 g
Carbohydrate	19 g
Fat	2 g

Kenny Miller

For a fresh drink I like:

milk + banana = milkshake

44

My favourite dinner after a game?

salad

+

steak

For lunch I like:

tomatoes

pasta

chicken

FResh FRuit Salad
Kenny Miller

Pineapple
1, peeled, cored,
sliced and cut
into small pieces

Grapes
16, sliced

Strawberries
16, sliced

Mango
2, peeled and sliced

Kiwis
4, peeled, sliced and cut
into small pieces

Mix the ingredients and enjoy it!!

Cooking time
0 mins

Preparation time
15 mins

Serves
4
children

Per child portion

Energy	488 kj
	114 kcal
Protein	2 g
Carbohydrate	27 g
Fat	0.6 g

Marcos Antonio Senna da Silva

For breakfast before a game I like:

cereal + milk

fruit, lots of fruit!

How does a healthy diet help me play well?

Natural foods are a great source of strength and energy. That's why I try not to eat too many pastries as they are rather unhealthy.

WORLD HEART FEDERATION®

Ingredients I really love:

tomatoes

Iberian ham

For a fresh drink I like:

different types of fruit juice to replenish my body naturally with the lost fluids and glucose

Who cooks my favourite food?

My wife who prepares traditional Brazilian dishes.

How is my cooking?

I am crazy about cooking pasta with tomato sauce and different kinds of vegetables.

UEFA we care

Swordfish and Vegetables

Marcos Antonio Senna da Silva

Mushrooms
200 g, halved

Swordfish
2 steaks,
150–175g each

Cucumber
½, chopped

Cherry tomatoes
12, halved

Fresh parsley
a large bunch, chopped

Garlic cloves
2, peeled and
chopped fine

Lemon ½

Asparagus
8 spears, halved

Olive oil
4 tbsp

Onion
1, cut in wedges

In a bowl make a marinade by mixing together the oil, lemon juice, garlic and parsley.

Place the 2 swordfish steaks on a plate, pour half the marinade over the fish and leave for about 20 to 30 minutes.

Mix all the vegetables in a bowl with the rest of the marinade.

Heat a frying pan over a medium-high heat. When hot add the vegetables. Cook them quickly, stirring a few times until they are just soft. Keep the vegetables warm while cooking the fish.

Heat a dry griddle pan or heat the same frying pan as used for the vegetables over a high heat. When the pan is very hot place the swordfish steaks carefully in it. Cook for a few minutes, and then turn the swordfish over carefully. The fish is cooked when it flakes easily but is still moist inside.

Serve half a swordfish steak per child and with lots of vegetables. Season with pepper if you want.

Cooking time
20 mins

Preparation time
30 mins

Serves
4
children

Per child portion

Energy	940 kj
	225 kcal
Protein	17 g
Carbohydrate	6 g
Fat	15 g

Ruud van Nistelrooy

For breakfast before a game I like:

cereal or muesli with milk, and orange juice

Ingredients I really like?

fresh fruit, salmon, tomatoes and Iberian ham

WORLD HEART FEDERATION®

How does a healthy diet help me play well?

The better you eat, the fitter you are!

Favourite dishes when I was a kid?

& **my mother's vegetable soup!**

Steak with vegetables and baked potatoes

Who cooks my favourite food?

My mother and my wife!

My cooking?

Very good!! My favourite dishes include grilled salmon or pasta with bolognese sauce.

UEFA
we care

Salmon Grilled with Cloves, served with Vegetables

Ruud van Nistelrooy

Salmon
2 fillets

Celery
1 stalk, chopped

Olive oil
½ tbsp

Leek
1, sliced (white end)

Red onion
1, sliced

Cloves
about 3-4 per fillet

Push the cloves into each salmon fillet and grill to taste.

Grill or sauté the vegetables in a little olive oil.

Remove the cloves and serve half a fillet per child with the vegetables.

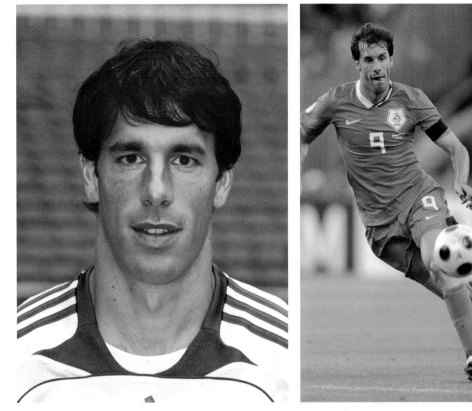

Cooking time
10 mins

Preparation time
10 mins

Serves
4
children

Per child portion

Energy	319 kj
	77 kcal
Protein	7 g
Carbohydrate	2 g
Fat	5 g

Steven Gerrard

My Favourite ingredients?

fish,

pasta,

chicken,

salad,

vegetables ...

especially
tomatoes

WORLD HEART FEDERATION®

MY FAVOURITE FRUIT?

oranges,

tangerines,

melon

and grapes

MY FAVOURITE drinks?

water
and
milk

Eating all these healthy foods will be good for your game.

Playing a footy match is a great way to keep fit and healthy.

Water is a major part of a healthy diet and exercise.

we care

CRunchy Sea BReam with HeRbs
Steven Gerrard

Thyme
1 small sprig,
fresh, chopped

White sea bream fillets
2

Olive oil
3 tbsp

Flat-leaf parsley
1 sprig, fresh, chopped

Lemon
1, juiced

Fresh rosemary
1 tbsp, chopped

Garlic cloves
2, peeled and chopped

Breadcrumbs
40 g

Heat oven to 180°C.

Chop 1 garlic clove and mix with the rosemary, parsley and thyme.

Place the herbs between the fish fillets.

Place the fish in an ovenproof dish.

Season and sprinkle with the breadcrumbs.

Mix the olive oil, lemon juice, 2 tbsp of water and 1 garlic clove.

Pour the mixture over the fish and bake for 20 minutes.

Cooking time
20 mins

Preparation time
12 mins

Serves
4
children

Per child portion

Energy	710 kj
	170 kcal
Protein	12 g
Carbohydrate	8 g
Fat	10 g

Yoann Gourcuff

For breakfast before a game I like:

cereal with milk, and orange juice

For lunch I like:

pasta, particularly pasta al'arrabiata

How does a healthy diet help me play well?

I feel physically good, light and full of energy. A balanced diet provides me with all the energy I need and helps me to keep going.

WORLD HEART FEDERATION®

60

FOR a REFRESHING drink I like:

Sparkling mineral water or water with a dash of lemon juice

Who cooks my favourite food?

My mum, whenever I return home to Brittany.

How is my cooking?

Not all that good... But I do know how to cook pasta and fry eggs.

GIRONDINS DE BORDEAUX
F C 1881

UEFA
we care

Spaghetti al'Arrabiata with Vegetables and Tuna

Yoann Gourcuff

Parmesan cheese
4 tbsp, grated

Spaghetti
160 g (dried)

Olive oil
2 tbsp

Spring onions
4–5 small or 1 large,
sliced or finely chopped

Tinned tuna
approx. 185 g
(including the oil / brine)

Courgettes
1–2, chopped

Chilli flakes
½ tsp
(optional to make it
more spicy)

Tomato puree
30 ml / 2 tbsp

Peeled tomatoes
1 tin of 400 g, chopped

Green or yellow pepper
1, chopped

Heat the olive oil in a pan over a medium heat.

Before it gets too hot, add the onions and cook for about a minute.

Add the courgettes, peppers and chilli flakes if you want and cook all together for a few minutes more.

Stir in the chopped tomatoes and the tomato puree.

Cook gently for about 15 minutes until slightly thickened.

rain and add the tuna to the sauce. Cook for a few minutes more to heat through.

While the sauce is cooking, bring lots of water to a vigorous boil in a large pot. d all the spaghetti at once and bring the pot of water quickly back to the boil. Give the pasta a good stir to make sure it does not stick. Cook for the time suggested on the spaghetti packet or about 5-10 minutes.

When cooked, drain the spaghetti into a colander and divide between four plates. Top with the sauce and sprinkle with the grated Parmesan cheese if you want.

 Cooking time
20 mins

 Preparation time
15 mins

Serves
4
children

Per child portion

Energy	973 kj
	231 kcal
Protein	13 g
Carbohydrate	25 g
Fat	9 g

WATER

VEGETABLES

FRUIT

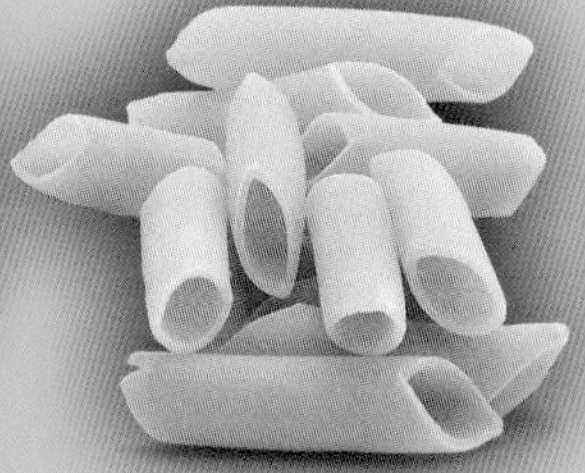

PASTA, RICE, POTATOES

CEREALS, BREAD

Food Tips

Eggs, Pulses, Nuts, Seeds

Fish, Chicken, Meat

Milk, Yoghurt, Cheese

Fat, Sugar, Salt

Water has no calories, sugar or caffeine.

Not drinking enough can affect performance and health.

Drink more water in hot weather or when very active.

WATER

Drink water **regularly.**

Limit those sugary, high-calorie caffeinated drinks.

Eat different colours – try dark green and orange!

5 a day of fruit and vegetables keeps you feeling good – and looking good!

Help keep the body healthier and happier.

Tuck into some tasty seasonal vegetables.

Eat one or two vegetables at every meal.

Vegetables

Eat vegetables as a quick snack, in curries, in pita bread, in sauces, in casseroles, or rolled into tortillas.

Aim for **variety** and fruit in season.

Enjoy fruit as snacks and at meals.

Try different **colours!**

Fruit is a great source of **fibre,** which helps digestion.

FRUiT

5 a day of fruit
and vegetables
keeps you feeling good
– and looking good!

Be creative:
fresh, dried, juice, fruit salads!

These foods are filling and full of energy.

Eat chips as an occasional treat.

Pasta, Rice, Potatoes

These foods are easy to cook!

Try them in salads, stir-fried,

in curries,

in sauces or in casseroles.

74

Eat wholegrain bread and cereals for extra **fibre.**

Cereals and bread are **filling** and full of energy.

Cereals, Bread

Try different types of bread and cereals:

light meals   breakfasts

snacks   porridge in winter

These foods are **great for** growing **bodies!**

They're easy to prepare!

Regularly replace meat with pulses, nuts, seeds or tofu.

Eggs, Pulses, Nuts, Seeds

Eggs can make a really **healthy** meal.

As healthy snacks:
in salads,
in casseroles,
for breakfast.

Fish, chicken and meat are **great builders for body and blood!**

Remove skin from poultry.

Oily fish is **very healthy.**

Try sardines on **toast.**

Make fish part of your regular diet.

Use lean meat.

Fish, Chicken, Meat

Careful – meat products can be really high in fat!

The amount of fat can vary a lot – choose low-fat dairy foods or eat small portions.

These foods are really needed for **strong bones and teeth.**

Milk, Yoghurt, Cheese

Soya milk is a great non-dairy option.

Try them as **snacks** or in **drinks.**

These foods have a lot of **fat, sugar and salt** but few other nutrients the body needs.

It's easy to eat too many of these high-calorie foods – limit how much you eat!

They do not help you to keep fit and on top form.

Food and Drinks High in FaT, SuGaR and/or SalT

There's no need to add salt to foods.

Check labels — some foods have a lot of salt and sugar!

we care

Keeping the people of Europe healthy is a vital concern for everyone who cares about the future of the continent and the quality of life of its inhabitants.

The health of our population affects the development of football, the pool of future players and the standard of our game.

While technology and economic development have changed and improved our lives, they have also changed the nature of our illnesses.

The biggest threat to our health no longer comes from what we might catch; instead it comes from our own choices about eating, drinking, or smoking – and the sedentary habits that we have adopted.

To protect our health in the 21st century, we must minimise these health threats as a top priority.

This is a challenge that football is already helping Europe to face.

As the world's most popular sport, football makes a great contribution to the health and fitness of the population.

The 23 million players who are registered for organised football activities on the continent are only a fraction of the Europeans who exercise regularly because they love the sport.

The importance of football as a means of keeping fit has increased as our work and transport require less physical effort. As the number of overweight and obese people continues to increase at an alarming rate, access to sports activities is not just a question of culture or leisure; it is imperative for preserving health and protecting economic growth.

But exercise is only half the fitness equation.

Without attention to diet, exercise alone can do little to counter the rising numbers of overweight and obese people.

As families have less time to prepare and eat meals together, our mothers' and grandmothers' cooking is no longer the main standard that shapes our food preferences, and our rich and varied culinary traditions are losing ground to easier but less healthy alternatives.

Football players have great potential to influence popular tastes and preferences, especially among the young.

With this power comes the responsibility to act as appropriate role models.

It is hoped that this book will help to tap football's potential for promoting the foods that make our players the strong and healthy athletes they are, and to offset the promotion of foods which contribute to the health problems that threaten our future.

Michel Platini
UEFA President

WORLD HEART FEDERATION®

A healthy heart is vital for living life to the full. In today's world, heart health is one of the main influences on the length and quality of people's lives.

The habits that determine our heart health are formed in childhood. As people become less active and unhealthy diet becomes more popular, it gets harder and harder to teach our children the habits that will help them live long, healthy lives.

The growing problem of childhood obesity is the measure of that challenge. If we wish for our children to grow up healthy, we must work together to stop this epidemic.

Physical activity is half of the equation of preventing obesity, and football is a great way to keep boys and girls active. The other half of the equation is a healthy diet. *Eat for Goals !* presents children with foods that their favourite players eat and enjoy, and shows them how to make them. Conveying the concept of balancing energy in (what we eat and drink) with energy out (how we exercise), it equips children with the preferences, knowledge and skills that are a foundation for a healthy diet.

Committed to promoting a healthy lifestyle among children and their families, the World Heart Federation works to promote policies and practices that make healthy choices easy choices. Working with UEFA has been a great privilege: it offers a unique chance to use the power of their passion for football to steer children toward healthy diets and healthy futures.

Like playing football, eating healthy food is not just healthy: it's fun! So learn what foods the football stars love, then cook them for your family and eat them to your heart's content.

Enjoy!

86

Dr Pekka Puska

President
World Heart Federation

EUROPEAN COMMISSION

GET ACTIVE!!!

It is my very great pleasure to introduce this compilation of footballers' recipes, supported by UEFA and the World Heart Federation.

With widespread reports in the media about the rise in obesity, there is a renewed public focus on diet and health. In bringing together footballers' favourite recipes this book brings to mind both food and exercise. As the European Health Commissioner I pay particular attention to the promotion of healthy diets and physical activity, and I welcome this effort, which combines these two areas. Clearly, both are essential for a healthy lifestyle.

As the Commissioner for Health, I can see how the diet of Europeans in all countries has been worsening in recent decades and how important it is for society to support individuals and families so they continue to eat well. It is clear to me that we must be proactive in Europe if we are to turn around these frightening trends. A balanced diet is very important for one's health. Eating well can reduce the likelihood of serious illnesses, such as cardiovascular disease, high blood pressure and many kinds of cancers.

At the European Commission we are doing our part. In May 2007, the European Commission published a strategy for Europe to tackle these issues in the form of a White Paper. The paper sets out the Commission's actions across the full range of its policies: from developing the best labelling for food products in shops, to encouraging the development of cycle paths and playgrounds in the EU. Moreover, we are putting renewed efforts into working with a range of actors such as the food industry, and with governments across the EU to push for change.

The world of football has long inspired us to exercise. Not content with this, it now seems to have set out to inspire us to eat well too. I can only applaud this initiative and look forward to tasting the results.

Androulla Vassiliou

European Commissioner
for Education, Culture,
Multilingualism and Youth

Glossary

P8, 78: Lean meat
Meat with a low-fat content and / or visible fat trimmed from the meat.

P8, 76, 77: Pulses
A food group that includes lentils, chickpeas, split peas, dried peas.

P9, 66, 67, 82: Calories
The amount of 'energy' released from carbohydrate, fat and protein is measured in kilocalories (kcal) or kilojoules (kJ). Kilocalories are often shortened to 'calories' to show the amount of energy a food supplies. Sometimes the term 'energy' is used in place of calories.

P9: Sodium
Sodium chloride is commonly known as salt. Sodium and chloride both help to keep the level of fluids in the body balanced. Chloride helps the body digest the food because it's an essential component of the juices in the stomach and intestines. It's the sodium part of salt we generally get too much of and this can cause high blood pressure (hypertension) which can increase our chances of having a stroke or heart attack.

P9, 66, 67: Caffeine
Found in tea, coffee and cola drinks, it usually makes the body produce more urine and thus you pee more depending on how much and how often you have caffeine. It's okay to drink these but it's best to drink only small amounts and drink plenty of water.

P13: Nigella
A dark spice similar to the cumin family.

P14 to 62: Tbsp
Tablespoon - a standard measure used in cooking.

P20: Sushi
Cold boiled rice moistened with rice vinegar, usually shaped into bite-size pieces and topped with raw seafood (nigiri-zushi) or formed into a long seaweed-wrapped roll, often around strips of vegetable or raw fish, and sliced into bite-size pieces (maki-zushi).

P20, 30, 31, 38, 39: Al dente
Used to describe the texture of pasta (and risotto rice) as tender or soft on the outside but with some resistance when bitten into.

P21: Smoothie
A smoothie is a type of cold drink similar to milkshakes made from a liquid (either milk, fruit juice, or water), crushed ice or ice cubes, and different fruit. Sometimes other foods are added, such as yoghurt, honey, maple syrup or ice cream. Smoothies are blended with an electric blender until the fruit and ice is puréed (made smooth).

P21, 44: Milkshake
Milkshakes are also a cold drink made with an electric blender. Milkshakes are usually made with milk, ice cream, and sweet syrups, such as chocolate syrup.

P29, 30: Alla Siciliana
Sicilian style - typically spicy.

P49: Glucose
Carbohydrates (starch and sugar) in food are converted to glucose
(or simple sugar) during digestion and carried in the blood to the body cells
to produce energy.

P49, 52: Iberian ham
Spanish ham, salted and air cured/dried. It has a unique taste and 'melt
in the mouth' flavour - regarded as the best cured ham in the world.

P51: Marinade
Placing fish, meat or vegetables in a highly seasoned and flavoured liquid
(the marinade) usually containing oil, wine or lemon juice, herbs and spices,
in order to tenderise and add flavour.

P54, 55: Salmon fillet
Slice of salmon, trimmed and cleaned of bones.

P55: Sauté
Lightly fry in a pan with a small amount of oil.

P59: Season
Adding a light amount of salt, pepper, herbs and spices usually at the end
of cooking so the dish can be tasted first to see what may need to be added
to improve its taste.

P60, 62: Al'arrabiata
A kind of sauce for pasta with lots of spices, particularly chillies,
garlic and pepper.

P70, 74: Fibre
The undigested parts of plant foods. It helps the body digest food better
and because it is bulky, gives a feeling of fullness.

P74: Wholegrain
All parts of the grain (whether wheat, oats, rye or other grains) are used
and nothing taken away.

P76: Tofu (also called bean curd)
An important protein source in oriental cooking. It's made from cooked soya
beans, is quite bland in flavour and responds well to marinades. Good for stir
frying, barbecuing and grilling; it's also high in calcium and vitamin E and low
in saturated fats.

P78: Poultry
A group of food - domestic birds - including chicken, duck, ostrich, turkey etc.

P82: Nutrients
Nutrients help to provide the body with the fuel it needs to work properly and
to stay healthy. They include vitamins, minerals, carbohydrate, fat and protein,
all found in food and drinks.

Index

Abbas Suwan 10, 12, 13, 14, 15
Androulla Vassiliou 88, 89
Apples .40
Apricots 34, 35
Asparagus. 50
Aubergines 22, 30, 31
Avocados 24, 26
Bananas 18, 19, 21, 25, 40, 44
Basil 30, 31
Beef 13, 24, 36
Birgit Prinz. 10, 16, 17, 18, 19
Black olives 30
Bolognese sauce 53
Boston Breakers 11
Bread 8, 33, 69, 74, 75
Breadcrumbs. 58, 59
Breakfast 18, 32, 36, 48, 52, 60, 75, 77
Brazil nuts. 38
Caffeine 9, 66, 67
Calories. 9, 66, 67, 82
Carles Puyol 10, 20, 21, 22, 23
Carrots .40
Casseroles. 69, 73, 77
Cathrine Paaske Sørensen 10, 24, 25, 26, 27
Cereals .8, 18, 19, 48, 52, 60, 74, 75
Cheese .8, 62, 63, 81
Chelsea FC 11
Cherry tomatoes 50
Chips 72
Chicken. 8, 12, 16, 26, 40, 42, 43, 44, 45, 56,
                                            78, 79
Chicken salad 26
Chicken salad sandwich. 42
Chillies. 32
Chilli flakes 62, 63
Chocolate 16
Cloves. .54, 55
Cocopops 32
Courgettes. 62, 63
Couscous 14, 15

Cucumber. 14, 15, 26, 50
Cumin. .13
Curries .69, 73
Curry powder 26
Dairy foods 80
Dressing 15, 26, 27, 38, 39
Eggs 8, 24, 61, 77
European Commission 88, 89
Fabio Cannavaro 10, 28, 29, 30, 31
Fat 9, 42, 79, 80, 82, 83
FC Barcelona. 10
FC Girondins de Bordeaux 11
1. FFC Frankfurt. 10
Fibre 70, 74
Fish. 8, 12, 16, 24, 28, 29, 33, 51, 56, 59,
                                            78, 79
Fortuna Hjørring FC 10
Frank Lampard 11, 32, 33, 34, 35
Fruit 7, 16, 17, 20, 34, 35, 36, 46, 48, 49,
                                            52, 57, 68, 70, 71
Fruit salad 46, 71
Fruitshake 25
Garlic (cloves) 26, 27, 30, 31, 50, 51, 58, 59
Glasgow Rangers FC 11
Glucose. 49
Grapes .46, 57
Hamburg SV 11
Heurelho da Silva Gomes 11, 36, 37, 38, 39
Honey. .13
Iberian ham. 49, 52
Ihaoud Bnei Sakhnin FC. 10
Juice. 33, 36, 43, 49, 51, 52, 58, 59, 61, 71
Juventus FC. 10
Kelly Smith 11, 40, 41, 42, 43
Kenny Miller. 11, 44, 45, 46, 47
Kiwis. 38, 46
Lean meat. 8, 78
Leeks 54
Lemons. 14, 15, 50, 58, 59
Lemon juice 33, 51, 59, 61

Lentils 8, 12
Lettuce 14, 15, 40, 42, 43
Limes 42, 43
Liverpool FC 11
Mangoes. 21, 38, 46
Marcos Antonio Senna da Silva . . .11, 48, 49, 50, 51
Marinade. 51
Meat. 8, 76, 78, 79
Melons 25, 57
Michel Platini. 84, 85
Milk. 8, 17, 18, 19, 32, 37, 44, 48, 52, 57,
                                        60, 81
Milkshake 21, 44
Mint 14, 15
Mozzarella. 28, 32
Muesli 52
Mushrooms. 50
Nigella. 13
Nutrients 82
Nuts 8, 34, 76, 77
Olive bread 42, 43
Olive oil 14, 15, 22, 23, 30, 34, 50, 54, 55,
                                        58, 59, 62, 63
Onions. 30, 31, 40, 50, 63
Oranges 25, 57
Orange juice 32, 37, 52, 60
Pastries. 48
Porridge 75
Parma ham. 28
Parmesan cheese 62, 63
Parsley 14, 15, 50, 51, 58, 59
Pasta 8, 12, 13, 20, 22, 23, 28, 29, 30, 31, 34,
                                        35, 36, 37, 40, 45, 49, 53, 56, 60, 61,
                                        63, 73
Pekka Puska, Dr 86, 87
Peeled tomatoes 62
Pepper (black) 26, 27, 51
Peppers (green, red, yellow). 22, 62, 63
Pesto 22, 23
Pine nuts. 13, 38, 39
Pineapple 34, 46
Pita bread 69
Pizza. 28
Potatoes 8, 32, 53, 73
Poultry 78
Pulses. 8, 76, 77
Raisins 38, 39
Red onions 22, 26, 38, 54
Rice 8, 13, 73

Rigatoni. 29
Rosemary 58, 59
Ruud van Nistelrooy. 11, 52, 53, 54, 55
Salad 26, 27, 36, 38, 42, 45, 56, 73, 77
Salmon 52, 53, 54, 55
Salt. 9, 82, 83
Sardines 78
Sauce 12, 34, 49, 63, 69, 73
Sea bream 58, 59
Season 59
Seeds 8, 22, 76, 77
Smoothie. 21
Sodium 9
Soup. 12, 37, 53
Soya milk 81
Spaghetti. 62, 63
Spinach. 34, 35
Spring onions 62, 63
Steak 29, 45, 53
Steven Gerrard 11, 56, 57, 58, 59
Strawberries 18, 19, 21, 25, 46
Sugar 9, 66, 67, 82, 83
Sundried tomatoes. 26
Sushi. 20
Sweetcorn. 26
Swordfish 50, 51
Tabbouleh 14
Tangerines. 57
Thyme 58, 59
Toast. 78
Tofu 76
Tomatoes. 14, 15, 22, 24, 26, 28, 32, 38, 40, 42,
                                        43, 45, 49, 52, 56, 62
Tomato puree 62
Tomato sauce 12
Tortillas 69
Tottenham Hotspur FC. 11
Tuna 62
UEFA. 84, 85
Vegetables. 7, 16, 22, 23, 31, 33, 35, 49, 50, 51, 53,
                                        54, 55, 56, 62, 68, 69, 71
Villarreal FC 11
Walnuts. 13
Water 7, 9, 15, 23, 31, 39, 57, 59, 61, 63, 66, 67
Weetabix. 32
World Heart Federation 86, 87
Yoann Gourcuff. 11, 60, 61, 62, 63
Yoghurt 8, 26, 27, 32, 42, 43, 81

93

WORKING FOR
GALS

William Gaillard
UEFA, Director of Communications
Project Sponsor

Patrick Gasser
UEFA, Football and Social Responsibility Manager
Head of Project

Jonathan Hill
UEFA, Head of Brussels Office
Project Adviser

Helen Alderson
World Heart Federation, Chief Operating Officer
Project Adviser

Graham Minton
World Heart Federation, Director of Corporate Relations
Project Adviser

Mark Schumacher
Project and Launch Manager

Russell Stevens
Content and design development
Meuva el Volante

Kathy Cowbrough
World Heart Federation, Dietitian

Dr Franchek Drobnic
Health Adviser

Dr Luis Serratosa
Health Adviser

Paul Lafferty
Chef

George Whetter
Chef

Diego Rodriguez
Design coordination -
Mueva el Volante

Esteban Lopez
Layout designer - Mueva el Volante

Bruno Ferrari
Illustrator - Mueva el Volante

Gabriel Dante Macri
Online presentation - Mueva el Volante

Steven Russell
Food photography - Mueva el Volante

Cesar Capaso
Food photography - Mueva el Volante

UEFA Language Services

Mary-Laure Bollini
UEFA, Brand Management

Susanne Pollatschek
UEFA, Legal Counsel

A book with more than one goal!

The world of football has long inspired people of any age and gender to exercise and to care about having a healthy lifestyle. Not content with this, it now seems to have set out to inspire them to eat well too.

Fit & Healthy: UEFA will donate GBP 1 from the sale of each *Eat for Goals!* book in support of World Heart Federation programmes encouraging children to be physically active.

Eat for Goals!
Football Heroes' Healthy Recipes